A Friend for Max

Story by Annette Smith
Illustrations by Richard Hoit

"Grandad! Grandad!" shouted Max.
"Look at the big truck!
Some men are taking beds
into the house over the road."

"A new family is moving in,"
said Grandad.

A car came up the road
to the house.
A big boy and a big girl
got out of the car.

The children's father
got out of the car, too.

"Oh, Grandad," said Max.
"Some children are moving
into that house.
I want a friend to play with,
but they are too old for me."

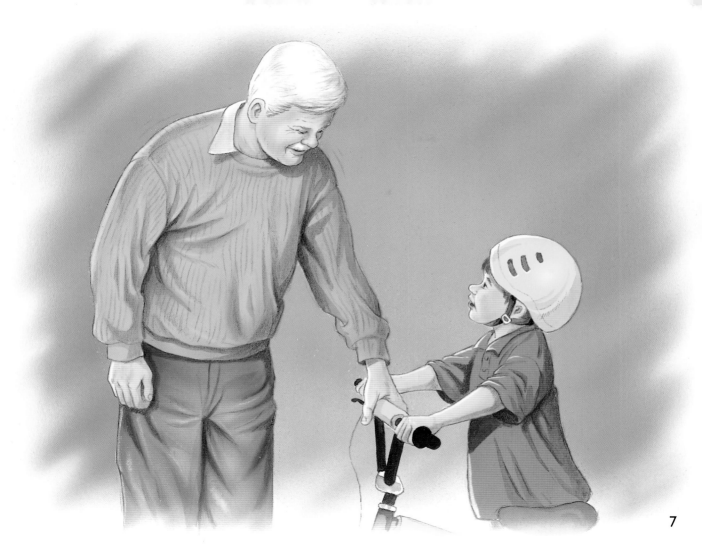

Grandad and Max
went to see the new family.

The big girl came to the door.
"Hello," she said. "I'm Hannah."

"Hello," said Max.
"I'm Max and I'm six."

Hannah looked at Max.

"I have a little brother called Jake," she said. "He is six like you. He is coming in Mum's car."

"Jake can come over to my place," said Max. "He can ride my bike."

The next day,
Hannah and Jake came to see Max.

Jake looked at Max's bike.
"I want to ride a bike like yours,"
he said, "but I can't."

"Grandad," said Max.

"Can you put the little wheels
back on my bike, please?
Then I can help Jake to ride it."

Grandad smiled at Max.

"Yes," he said.

"Go and get the little wheels.

They are in the shed."

"This is a good bike, Max,"
said Jake. "I like riding it."